Baby Eagles

from the song by
John Archambault and David Plummer

illustrated by
Jennifer Bolton

SRA
Macmillan/McGraw–Hill
Columbus, Ohio

Printed in the United States of America.

SRA Macmillan/McGraw-Hill
250 Old Wilson Bridge Road
Worthington, Ohio 43085

ISBN 0-02-685796-0

1 2 3 4 5 6 7 8 9 CDY 99 98 97 96 95 94

Baby eagles leave the nest one day.
Soar to the heavens,
that's the eagles' way.

Stretch your wings across the sky.
Sun on your wings,
eagle, fly high,
fly high.

Baby eagles leave the nest one day.
Soar to the heavens,
that's the eagles' way.
Baby eagle, eagle, look into my eye.
Baby eagle, eagle, eagle, fly high.
Fly high, high.
Baby eagle, baby eagle.

You nest in crags on barren cliffs.
One day, baby eagle,
you step to the edge of the nest.
You stretch your wings.
You fly.

Spiraling above the clouds to the heavens,
sunlight on your wings, baby eagle.
Show us the way to fly high.

Baby eagles leave the nest one day.
Soar to the heavens,
that's the eagles' way.
Stretch your wings across the sky.
Sun on your wings,
eagle, fly high,
fly high.

Baby eagles leave the nest one day.
Soar to the heavens,
that's the eagles' way.
Baby eagle, eagle, look into my eye.
Baby eagle, eagle, eagle, fly high.
Fly high, high.
Baby eagle, baby eagle.

Proud bird with treasured feather,
mighty talons.
You spiral above the valleys,
above the clouds.
Guardian of the sun.

Eagle, show us the way
with eagle eye to fly high.
Show us the way.

Baby eagles leave the nest one day.
Soar to the heavens,
that's the eagles' way.
Stretch your wings across the sky.
Sun on your wings,
eagle, fly high,
fly high.

Baby eagles leave the nest one day.
Soar to the heavens,
that's the eagles' way.
Baby eagle, eagle, look into my eye.
Baby eagle, eagle, eagle, fly high.
Fly high, high.
Baby eagle, baby eagle.